To renew any items:

- visit any Coventry Library

- go online to www.coventry.gov.uk/libraries

- telephone 024 7683 1999

SOD IT!

The Depression 'Virus' and how to deal with it

by Martin Davies

(Thanks to Wendy Bennett for editing this book and
keeping her sense of humour)

Also by Martin Davies

SOD IT ALL!

How to Deal with the Stress 'Virus' in your Life

Copyright © 2006 Martin Davies
Reprinted 2007

Published by SOD IT! BOOKS an imprint of   Talking Life
PO Box 1
Wirral CH47 7DD, England

ISBN 1 901 910 23 7

Printed and bound in Great Britain by
Bookmarque, Croydon, Surrey

FOR MORE INFORMATION ABOUT
SOD IT! BOOKS (+44) 0151-632-0662
www.sod-itbooks.co.uk
www.talkinglife.co.uk

SOD IT!

The Depression 'Virus' and how to deal with it

MARTIN DAVIES, RMN

ABOUT THE AUTHOR

Martin Davies, RMN, Dip. CPN., has worked in the UK National Health Service for over 25 years, coming from a psychiatric nursing background. He has worked in psychiatric wards and was a charge nurse in the community before moving into primary care. Most of his professional career was spent in GP surgeries before training and working as a counsellor.

For professional and personal reasons, he 'burned out' over a period of time and this resulted in several episodes of depression. Although maintaining his career, he became aware of the mistakes and errors he was making through this time.

A change of career led to him leading an educational project on depression, during which time he worked with many national figures and organisations, and speaking at major conferences and events. Working with supportive colleagues, and seeking good help, Martin worked through his depression and moved into training and education, developing a range of courses (and a 'unique training style'!). He now delivers courses and presentations throughout the UK on subjects including depression, stress, emotional intelligence, transactional analysis, teamworking and cognitive behavioural therapy and has co-written 2 books on stress in the workplace.

Although a health professional, Martin actually started his career in art. His illustrations and cartoons have become not only a personal way of releasing thoughts, feelings and ideas, but are incorporated in all of his courses and presentations.

As well as this book, Martin is the author of SOD IT ALL! How to deal with the stress 'virus' in your life.

He has been published in numerous national magazines, including Private Eye and has illustrated many more. Martin's cartoons are often amusing...but with serious messages! His work reflects his style and his passion about his subjects.

DEPRESSION

Depression is the most common long-term condition that there is, more common than asthma, diabetes, and heart disease. In adults it is associated with emotional damage to relationships, marital breakdown, long-term effects on children, sickness absence and a high labour turnover. In economic terms, it results in a loss of up to 35 million working days per year. More people die of depression than they do of asthma, diabetes and heart disease - yet resources, training and manpower are targeted at almost anything other than depression! The number of people who take their own lives as a result of depression is potentially the same number as 3 Jumbo jets crashing with a full payload every year!

The cost of depression in terms of human misery is incalculable, but in most cases it needn't be a long-term illness, as it can be prevented and treated - what a tragedy!

Depression is an illness with both physical and psychological symptoms and a wide range of causes. The effects of depression are felt much wider than the sufferers themselves - their families, friends, colleagues and children can all fall victim when in close or regular contact. It's almost as if depression were a form of 'virus' and no-one is safe from it!

Depression can 'infect' the young, the old, the rich and the poor. It does not respect culture, gender, or background. With a slow rate of onset, the symptoms may not become apparent until the virus is well-established…and it is HIGHLY contagious!

The virus responsible has now been identified:

THE DEPRESSION VIRUS

(Latin: JOYUS STRANGULATUS)

"What is the problem with depression?"

When someone says that they may be depressed, it can provoke a whole range of reactions from others, from shock and horror to utter blankness! Other people don't know what to do when someone says they are depressed, except perhaps to offer some tea and sympathy. Depression is a topic that isn't exactly 'sexy'!

The Breeding Ground?

> There are certain conditions that we breed well in.......

The virus is always on the look out for places to breed and multiply, like any virus. Certain 'conditions' will ensure mass reproduction....

People who are, for example:

o   Physically run down
o   Have low self-esteem and low confidence
o   Experiencing one major life event (e.g. bereavement, divorce, unemployment etc)
o   Going through several life events and traumas
o   Over-worked and stressed-out
o   Anxious and uptight all the time
o   In poor supportive environments
o   On their own
o   Not good at expressing their thoughts and feelings openly
o   Full of anger, resentment and unresolved issues

In fact, **ANYONE** who is either not looking after themselves or having a tough time in life is fair game and easy pickings!

The depression virus, once caught, attacks the body's immune system. Our immunity is not just about physical immunity - it's also about our emotional immunity...

The virus will attack and destroy what is left of this immunity, so any signs of weakness in any part of the body might attract this infectious character! Our physical immunity depends on:

o   Good balanced diet / adequate vitamins and minerals
o   Good hydration (plenty water/fluids)
o   Physical fitness / sufficient physical activity

Whilst our emotional immunity depends on:

o   Good coping skills
o   Problem solving ability
o   Supportive networks
o   Realistic/Positive Attitudes
o   Clear thinking
o   Insight and awareness
o   Knowledge and understanding
o   Confidence and a good self-esteem
o   Sense of humour and a sense of perspective

A healthy state of mind!

When someone is well, physically, emotionally and psychologically looking after theirself, the body produces a range of chemicals that keeps their health in check, in balance. In depression this balance of body chemistry is upset, thus producing symptoms. The brain is a bit like a petrol tank in a car - it needs a good level of 'petrol' (or brain chemicals) to keep running properly. Just as a car that runs low on petrol starts to falter - to become erratic and eventually stop, these natural brain chemicals are needed to keep a person running. These chemicals are called neuro-transmitters. Examples of these neurotransmitter chemicals are **SEROTONIN** and **NORADRENALINE**. These chemicals, amongst other functions, affect one's mood, thinking and ability to cope.

Has your body's 'petrol tank' got enough in it to run or is it on 'reserve', or even on EMPTY?

Body chemistry is the FOOD for MOOD!

Well-stocked:

On reserve supply:

As someone starts to become low in mood and spirits, their brain chemistry alters too, **the brain needs topping up!**

Depression is a physical illness too!

A healthy body and brain require a good level of these natural chemicals - just as a car needs topping up with oil, water, antifreeze and petrol. The body needs good nutrients and to be treated with care and kindness.

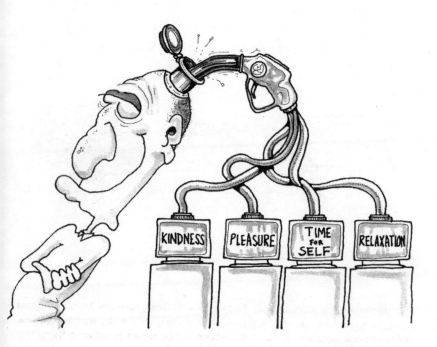

No-one knows if it's the depression that causes the level of Serotonin to drop, or whether it's the lowering of Serotonin that causes the depression, it's the ol' 'chicken and egg' problem!

Multiplication and further infection!

As the virus enters the body, it doesn't take long before it starts to multiply - but it can take weeks or even months for symptoms to appear. It is a slow-acting virus that gradually eats away at what is left of our defences.

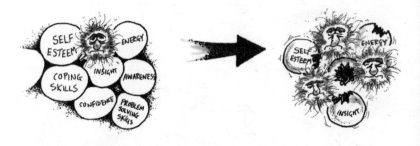

As it eats away and multiplies, so feelings of well-being diminish. Moods become erratic and generally more pessimistic and thought processes start to run riot. Ability to cope becomes harder and one may become over-sensitive to things that normally one can deal with.

As Serotonin drops, so does mood, confidence, activity levels and sense of humour, and sleeping and eating patterns alter.

The VACUUM CLEANER of life!

Life, work and relationships can <u>suck the goodness out</u> of the best of us - modern living has created ever increasing demands. **More** is expected, **quicker** and with **less** regard for one's well-being. If the vacuum cleaner of life sucks **too** much out of us (without the precaution of being topped up) we will be running on empty.

Working too hard with few stops or lunch breaks, not giving attention to relationships or life interests and not looking after oneself, will result in a serious neglect of mental health. We need to take stock and look at how to fill the tank back up!

The RESERVOIR OF RESILIENCE

Human beings are a bit like a reservoir, when full of water we are beautiful, but when empty we are nasty sludge! Being 'full' is having lots of coping methods, looking after ourselves and having good, supportive relationships. The vacuum cleaner of life can suck the goodness out, leaving one empty; empty people are not pleasant to be around and they themselves feel like nasty sludge. It is very important to keep your reservoir topped up.

THE RESERVOIR OF RESILIENCE

Healthy (Full)

Unhealthy (Empty)

How is **YOUR** reservoir?
Does it need topping up?
What do you need more of, what is lacking?

The ICEBERG of depression!

Becoming depressed is usually a process that has taken a bit of time to get to - it doesn't just happen! It is often an accumulation of events and circumstances, a build up of unresolved or insoluble difficulties. This build-up is often quite personal - that is, no-one else quite knows or understands what is going on inside the depressed person's mind. All others see is the outside face that someone with depression wears. Sooner or later the real stuff bubbles up and comes out.

There is only so much people can take before the end result of bottling things up starts to show itself. The build-up of tension, anger, injustice, worry or gloom presents itself, often in unpleasant ways for the recipients. Do not judge people on what you see - what you see is often not a true representation of the whole person. Helping people find ways of <u>resolving the issues</u> that have built up is very important.

So, what is depression?

Imagine a ruler which at one end (0 to say 4) represents feeling a bit "down" and low. Whilst the other end (say 7 to 12) represents the worst kind of deep depression. It's important to realise that everyone moves along this sliding scale of a ruler at some point - everyone gets down from time to time. But as we move along this ruler, the chemicals responsible for mood get more and more out of balance.

Depression can be divided into three levels:

o   **MILD**
o   **MODERATE**
o   **SEVERE**

Mild depression is experienced by everyone from time to time - it's a normal lowering of mood and in most cases passes within a few hours, days or a week or so. Antidepressants are of NO use yet.

Moderate depression is an abnormal lowering of mood - a much more extreme lowering that is the first sign of the illness of depression developing. Antidepressants are probably required.

Severe depression is abnormal low mood PLUS a distinct loss of day-to-day functioning - everyday activities are severely impaired!

The range of symptoms experienced in depression

In depression there are many symptoms, some unique to us as individuals and some common to us all - one person will undoubtedly experience depression differently from another - but there are some key symptoms to look out for.

- All slowed up (in actions and in thinking)
- Tiredness and/or anxiousness
- Poor concentration (short-term memory loss)
- Low mood / mood swings
- Tearful and upset
- Irritability, frustration and anger outbursts
- Loss of interest in sex
- Withdrawal from people and social situations
- Feeling worthless / guilty / hopeless
- Inability to work or do simple tasks
- A desire to escape, to leave, to die, to stop existing

Depressed people have said

"What's the point in anything - there doesn't seem to be any purpose anymore"

"I'll never get out of this…I'll never get better"

"Everything I think is just dark, black and miserable"

"No-one else could possibly understand how I feel - I just can't hold myself together anymore…I'm falling apart"

"I feel totally alone…helpless…isolated from everyone and everything"

"I am **SO** weak. I'm just a waste of space…pathetic!"

"This is truly madness - I must be mad…crazy"

"It's like being in dark treacle - I can hardly move. It's too difficult to even talk or think sometimes"

"I just don't feel anything…I'm empty…numb…cold"

"I don't feel any part of anything - I'm separate from everyone else as they get on with their lives…I might as well not be here"

"The old 'ME' has gone….I can't even remember what it's like to be ME"

On getting over depression people have said

"Colours have come back…the grey has gone!"

I SEE things clearly now…in focus and in so much detail"

"I am SO much stronger - I know myself SO much better now"

"That person has gone - I'm a new model…mark 2
………..and even better!"

"I can't believe the amount of energy I've got - where had it all gone?"

"Some things just don't seem so important now - not after having gone through
that Hell….I see things in a much better perspective"

"I FEEL again…..I hadn't realised how much I'd shut down!"

"It's like emerging from a nightmare"

"It's like someone's turned the light back on - I can see!"

Depression has an effect on all parts of the body and mind

THOUGHTS

FEELINGS

BEHAVIOURS

...WITHDRAWAL.....
..AVOIDANCE.... SLOWED UP....
....CLUMSY.... ANTISOCIAL...
...STOP DOING THINGS....

> The illness of depression has a list of symptoms that are well-recognised

The illness of MAJOR depression

(Moderate to Severe on the depression ruler scale) is:

A depressed mood or loss of interest and pleasure plus 4 or more of the following:

- Feelings of worthlessness
- Poor concentration
- Loss of energy and fatigue
- Thoughts of suicide
- Loss or increase in appetite/weight
- Loss or increase of sleep
- Anxiety, agitation or slowing up

This combination of symptoms <u>FOR A MINIMUM OF 2 WEEKS OR MORE</u> indicates that someone has the illness of depression.

THIS NEEDS TREATMENT!

Anxiety as part of depression

A common symptom of depression is anxiety. Anxiety and depression are easily mixed up - one can look like the other. It is important therefore for doctors to be able to distinguish one from the other. The treatment for anxiety is different to that of depression, and vice versa.

It is common for people to experience a mixed state...that is, they become depressed and anxious.

Some typical signs can be

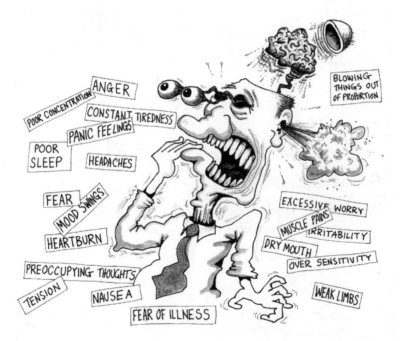

Constant worry and apprehension take their toll - people become tired and weary, thus feeding the depression. It is exhausting being uptight all the time, and it will also be likely you will infect others with your tension! The virus spreads and creates a **worse** atmosphere!

Physical health worries

Worries and concerns over physical health are common features of depression and anxiety - many of the common symptoms are indeed physical and can easily be misinterpreted as something more sinister.

Lack of factual knowledge, myths and information gleaned from popular magazines, T.V., Newspapers and the Internet, all contribute to mis-information. Many people are quite unaware that the biological changes that take place in the body when people are depressed also cause physical symptoms - **depression is not just an emotional illness!** Unless this is understood, it is easy to become preoccupied with the purely physical symptoms and seek help only for these.

The frequent attender!

Constant reassurance can become draining, not only for the poor sufferer, but for that person's immediate family, friends - and the doctor! Seeking further tests and investigations for those aches and pains only comes up with - nothing! Trouble is, although anyone can get a whole range of physical symptoms, they are not caused by disease or an ailment, they are caused by the biochemical changes that take place in the body when people become depressed. Therefore, any physical investigations will come up negative; nothing is actually wrong. This does NOT mean the symptoms are imaginary, it simply means they are **part** of the illness of depression and until the depression is treated and relieved, the physical symptoms may continue.

Continually talking about or asking about the physical symptoms only wastes time and energy. Asking for an explanation as to HOW physical symptoms can come about by being depressed would be far more helpful and it would also stop others being driven up the wall with the demands of someone seeking reassurance!

Common physical symptoms

Common physical symptoms include:

o   Headache
o   Muscular aches and pains (neck/back/chest)
o   Tiredness and lethargy
o   Gastric upset/pain
o   Sleep problems

Such problems often result in an increase in the taking of a range of medicines such as:

o   Painkillers (Paracetamol/codeine/ibuprofen/aspirin)
o   Antacids
o   Creams and gels (anti inflammatories)
o   Herbal remedies
o   Vitamins and 'natural' nutrients

Of course, some of the most common 'treatments' that are increased are alcohol, cigarettes and other drugs. It is possible to end up as a walking pharmacy!

Many of these 'treatments' actually also make depression worse

The on-going physical symptoms

If you bottle up emotions, unresolved difficulties or unspoken worries, the end result can mean they alter your brain and body chemistry so much that they start to produce real physical symptoms. It is common to experience headaches, for example, when worried about something. Men are particularly bad at expressing their worries and emotions (a surprise to you ladies, eh?!) - bottling things up can lead to **SOMATISATION:** physical symptoms as a result of built-up negative emotions.

There has to come a time when the REAL issues (the real causes) need to be addressed. Ignoring them or denying them will only maintain the physical aches and pains..and probably make them worse! For some, dealing with the real worries is simply too difficult. Not facing up to the real (emotional) pain can result in chronic illness

The 'FAT FILE' person

Not understanding what the illness of depression is, and seeking inappropriate (and often constant) reassurance can result in a more than average number of visits to the doctor - in turn resulting in the 'FAT FILE' syndrome, key features of which include:

- o Repeated visits to the doctor
- o Lists of symptoms presented
- o Seeing different (or all) doctors
- o Focussing on one or two particular symptoms
- o Focussing on physical symptoms only
- o Seeking constant investigations and tests
- o Increased number of prescriptions/over-the-counter medications

Trust the GP's judgement. Doctors always check out the possibility of underlying illnesses before discounting them. Avoid the constant referral to medical books and seeking further (physical) investigations. Find out about depression - ask relevant questions and **LISTEN!**

ACKNOWLEDGEMENT - the KEY!

Admitting to yourself that you may be depressed is the first and most important step to recovery. It's not easy and certainly not comfortable to talk about it with other people, for fear of their reaction. But it is without doubt **THE MOST IMPORTANT KEY STEP!** Denying it to oneself and to others only delays the healing and, worse, may increase the likelihood of a longer-term and more severe illness. It can take a little while to reach this step but it's well-worth reaching.

Acknowledgement is the first step towards **inoculation** against the virus, which will help build an **immunity** for further attacks!

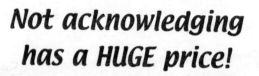

Not acknowledging has a HUGE price!

It takes some people years to reach a point where they can be open and acknowledge their illness - **WHAT A WASTE!** Weeks, months and years of misery and heartache. It can take a massive toll on the individual; job, income, family, children, future hopes, financial security etc. It can also have a devastating effect, in the long run, on personal relationships, friendships, and self-esteem. Once acknowledged, try to share this insight with partners, family, friends and work colleagues if appropriate.

"Keeping misery inside only rots us from the inside, it destroys all that there once was leaving only a shell on the outside: **you build your own prison!**"

MILD depression

Mild	Moderate	Severe

MILD depression is something everyone suffers from at some time or another - but it usually passes after a few hours, a few days or a week or so at most. It is a normal lowering of mood as a result of things that have been going on in someone's life. Perhaps this mild depressed state is a way of coping with difficult circumstances for some…a way of retreating from difficult times until things blow over.

VIRUS RATING

Although down and miserable, work is still entirely possible and indeed, although someone may feel quite wretched inside, others may not even detect what that person is going through as it is contained. <u>Mild depression does NOT need antidepressants.</u> Support, self-help, talking about things and taking things easy will all help us move through this state.

MODERATE depression

Mild	Moderate	Severe

Moderate depression is much more problematic; this is getting more serious and needs help. The feelings of mild depression are much deeper now and it's not shifting. Mood continues to fall well below what is normal and day-to-day activities are difficult to carry out. The simplest tasks can require huge amounts of effort and tiredness becomes the 'norm'. Things that can normally be shrugged off become intensely unbearable. This is the start of the 'illness' of depression and needs more specialised help.

VIRUS RATING

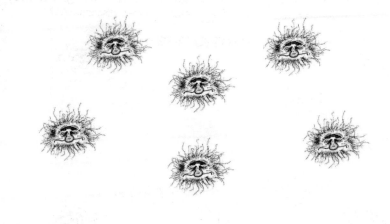

Moderate depression, although requiring more support and help, probably also needs medical treatment: antidepressants. The risk of not treating this with antidepressants early is a more severe illness.

SEVERE depression

Mild	Moderate	Severe

It doesn't get worse than this! Not only is mood abnormally low and unbearable, functioning will be at best extremely difficult, at worst impossible. Functioning means:

o   Day-to-day activities (eating/working/making decisions etc)
o   'Normal' activities such as sleeping/resting/job
o   Socialising and mixing with others

and in **SEVERE** depression all of these are far worse. Simple tasks such as getting up, washing, dressing and deciding what to wear, eating or making a cup of tea all become such an effort. Avoidance becomes the norm. This eventually isolates a person from others (although this may already be the case), and guilt and self-loathing is an everyday experience. The sufferer becomes 'disconnected'.

VIRUS RATING

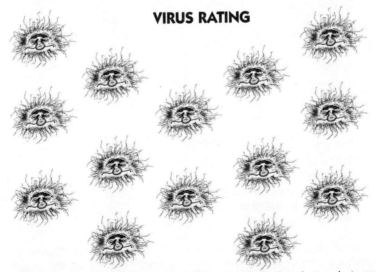

Severe depression always requires medication from the doctor, but may also require the help of a psychiatrist or in-patient treatment. Family and friends are vital for support and on-going help throughout.

What causes depression?

Seldom is depression caused by one single thing. Although it can be one event that triggers the illness, it is usually an accumulation of several events or triggers that result in depression. One of the most common causes is **LIFE EVENTS:**

Life throws a multitude of events at us that can bring us down:

o   Relationship difficulties & conflicts
o   Job / work / everyday demands
o   Health issues
o   Worries over children and family
o   Money and financial problems
o   Loss and bereavement

And it's not only bad things that cause distress, it can be good things like moving house, having a baby or getting married - nice, but very stressful, leading, in some cases, to not coping and depression. For a smaller number of people, depression is part of their genetic makeup - its in their genes (eg manic depression)

Lack of supportive network

It is incredibly important for human beings to have people around to rely on at times, to have friends, family or acquaintances to talk to. Being isolated and having few connections with other human beings is not good for anyone. Living a solitary life, physically or emotionally will take its toll!

Trouble is, when someone does become depressed , they are likely to withdraw further from any social situation or company, making support even more difficult to access. The depressed person will also make it more difficult for others to even try to help - depressed people become harder to talk to and create an atmosphere where others might find it too awkward to even attempt to communicate - thus making the situation worse!

Predisposing factors

There are some people, whether its because of circumstances or because of the kind of person they are, who are likely to become depressed more easily than others. For instance:

o   If there is a personal and/or family history of depression
o   If someone has lost a parent in childhood
o   Genetic predisposition

These and other factors raise the possibility of becoming more depressed than others who have not got these things in their past.

Certain groups of people, caught in certain circumstances, such as the homeless and single parents are also more likely to experience depression - due to isolation, hopelessness and poor supportive networks. Personality is also important - some people have more anxious personalities, some are pessimistic in nature. Living in a family where someone is chronically depressed can have a profound effect on others in the family; the virus spreads in families!

Long-term health problems

On-going or long-term illness and physical health problems can become a strain on the best of us - having a painful problem such as arthritis or back pain wears people down. Having to take medication every day and living a lifestyle which doesn't allow us to do the things we'd like to do is indeed depressing. Diabetes, heart disease and asthma are all life-long illnesses which can have the affect of lowering someone's mood (and the mood of those who are living with them too).

Depression itself also reduces one's ability to cope with pain (the chemical imbalances in the body which are involved in depression, reduce the chemicals responsible for dealing with pain), so any existing physically painful health problem will feel worse, and medication that once helped the pain will stop working.

"Why is it so hard to admit to not coping so well?"

Stigma and embarrassment, and the fear of what others may think, may cause many people to keep their personal worries to themselves. Some have said:

"They'll think I'm weak"
"I feel such a burden to everyone around me"
"I'm SO ashamed"
"I should be able to get out of this…but I can't!"

ATTITUDES to depression vary.

Attitudes are still very negative and based on myth rather than experience or fact. Most attitudes are fuelled by lack of knowledge and fear. Depression is not an illness that is openly talked about, like asthma or diabetes. Worry over what family, friends and colleagues may think may cause a great deal of private pain; even concern about what the doctor might think or say prevents many people seeking and obtaining help. The risk of not openly talking about things or seeking appropriate help is the development of a long-term and disabling illness. Some cultures actively suppress any evidence of emotional or mental ill-health.

Keeping things inside the family

For many families, and some cultures, keeping things inside the family (away from outsiders) is their way of dealing with things. This can be at best stifling, but at worst claustrophobic and even life-threatening. Protective families can deny genuine depressed people from receiving proper help - leading to them becoming **prisoners** within their own homes, becoming more detached and isolated. Not all families or cultures encourage outside help, in fact some actively avoid any outside influences. Some cultures are very suspicious of traditional Western health care. For some, the family can be the very source of their ill health.

It can be too threatening for some families to acknowledge that they are unable to help a member of their own - to accept that they are powerless, or worse that they are the cause. It can take a lot of persuasion (and courage) for a family or community to allow outside intervention. <u>Some don't survive</u>. So <u>all</u> opportunities should be tried to gain appropriate (confidential) help and treatment. Not always easy!

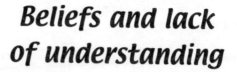

Beliefs and lack of understanding

The belief that depression is not a 'proper' illness and that it is a sign of personal character weakness still causes problems even in the 21st Century.

The old macho image is still with us! High expectations, unrealistic demands, the aura of toughness. Regardless of gender, modern society expects far too much of people and the cost is high.

It is the strong person who seeks help - it takes a lot of courage to acknowledge a problem and to ask for help. It is much easier to ignore, deny and rationalise a way through life.

Myths

Myths are perpetuated by ignorance and fear. Modern media contributes to this by reinforcing terminology:

"Mad"
"Neurotic"
"Stupid"
"Pathetic & weak"

Being neurotic implies a lack of moral fibre, an in-built weakness and being pathetic. But history is littered with individuals who have suffered from depression who are anything but lacking in strength. Sir Winston Churchill and Queen Victoria are two notable examples.

Depression is a real illness with real signs and symptoms, with real consequences <u>and there are real treatments available.</u>

"Just snap out of it!"

Can someone just "snap out of" diabetes, asthma or flu? Of course they can't! Unlike diabetes and asthma though, depression CAN be treated and may never return. Most people who suffer depression would be only too glad to snap out of it if they could.

In severe depression it is simply impossible to carry out even the simplest tasks or day to day activities, far less do a day's work! People who have not experienced depression may not understand why it is so difficult to make decisions, why it's so hard to even smile, or why it is impossible to get out of bed. In mild to moderate depression individuals might be able to work and function to some level, but the cost is high, tiredness and lethargy may be overwhelming.

Are you living with a stranger?

It can be extremely difficult (and depressing) living with someone who is depressed - even worse if they have not yet acknowledged that they need help. The depressed person has lost their old persona and have become someone else. It is not that they have permanently lost their old self, it is just hidden away.

If you are living with someone who is depressed, you also need help, advice and support. Do not be put off asking for help, for **you** might be the very person who is to <u>lead the hunt</u> to find the depressed person's old self. Without guidance and direction it can be a difficult task
There is no MAP with specific instructions!

Why depression can be missed

1. What the person does to stop others picking it up

- ○ Smiles…doesn't LOOK depressed
- ○ Not mentioning anything about their feelings
- ○ Focus on physical health or physical symptoms
- ○ Not understanding that it might be depression
- ○ Poor knowledge about depression
- ○ Believing that others are not interested
- ○ Not wanting to take up others time by talking about it
- ○ Putting it down to something else

"I'm fine…just a bit tired these days"
"I'm probably a bit run down…it'll pass"
"It's my age you know!"
"Think it's just this bad back of mine getting me down"

2. What doctors do that causes depression to be missed

○   Not looking at the person in front of them - no eye contact
○   Showing signs of hurry - putting the person off
○   Not asking the right questions
○   Not listening to what the person is actually saying
○   Asking questions that just require a "Yes" or a "No" answer
○   Focussing on physical things
○   Being miserable themselves - not in the mood to tackle depression

3. What can happen in a consultation that prevents depression being picked up

o   When interruptions occur
o   When silences are not tolerated
o   When empathy is not shown by the doctor
o   When non-verbal signs are not noticed
o   When no-one mentions anything emotional
o   When the environment is not comfortable

Time!

Doctors and nurse may be frustrated at their own lack of knowledge, skills and a plain lack of time to deal with depression.

GP's time is limited and recognising this helps. Talking around the houses not getting to the point only wastes time and often causes frustration in the GP or nurse too! Try to be clear and precise, get to the point quickly. Perhaps even work out beforehand what you will say and how you will say it - even write a short note of your symptoms or what has been going on?

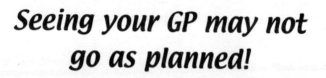

Seeing your GP may not go as planned!

Even the best plans can go astray, it might not be YOUR best moment, it might not be the doctor's best time! What is said by all may not be quite what is anticipated, and the responses may not be what was expected.

Although GPs should be sympathetic, it is known that not everyone may respond in the manner that one would like. Some doctors give the impression of fobbing you off, or may not appreciate quite how bad a patient is feeling. If you feel your doctor is not the sort of person you can be open with, or you have had a negative experience before - then ask to see a different doctor. It can be helpful to ask which doctor might have a particular interest in depression. Don't just put up and shut up - but remember that doctors and nurses need you to help them. Always be sympathetic to the doctor's moods too!

"Who do I see?"

There are many interested doctors and nurses around, so don't be put off at the first obstacle. It's important to seek out someone that you can feel comfortable with. Not all doctors have the experience or ability to deal with depression, just as not all doctors are experienced with asthma, diabetes or sport's injuries - they all have their own areas of expertise and interest like the rest of us.

Ask at the surgery or ask friends. Perhaps a particular doctor can be recommended. Sometimes its easier to speak to someone of the same gender and don't forget about the practice nurses who are often just as skilled as the medical staff and can sometimes be more approachable.

There's no <u>gain</u> to being depressed - <u>is there?</u>

Although a small number of depressed people will need on-going long-term treatment, most will get better with the right help. It can be comforting to have others look after us, nurture us and do things for us when we are unwell (who doesn't enjoy a bit of pampering?!) but for some, the gain is **SO** powerful that it is counter-productive to get better.

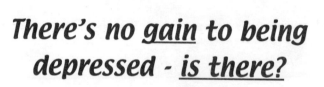

> Yes....they've tried everything - nothing seems to work....I'll probably need help for the rest of my life....

Reliance on others is not helpful. There comes a point when you need to start doing things for youself..even if it feels uncomfortable. It can become too rewarding to be **"ill"**, and some people can really milk it!   Watch out for those who manipulate others into providing help - it does not do them any good.   It might mean appearing a bit 'hard'.

Try and see:
o   Are there any triggers that lower/improve your mood?
o   When is your mood Low/High?
o   Are there any **PATTERNS** emerging from your mood chart?

Improving your immunity to the 'virus'!

This is advice for people with **MILD** depression.

Acknowledge...acknowledge... acknowledge!

To get better and to stay better, it's **SO** important to continually acknowledge one's emotional state - whether good or not so good.
This is also a good way to **MONITOR YOURSELF.**

Every so often take a look at how you are doing, perhaps even start a **MOOD DIARY** (see page 87) and chart your day-to-day progress, remember though that there will be times when things feel as if they are sliding back - this is NORMAL and to be expected. Progress isn't just about getting better, it's about working through the not-so-good moments too, and **learning from these.**

Understanding and knowledge is WISDOM!

It's very difficult to deal with something that is not understood - imagine a mechanic trying to fix an engine that he does not have any knowledge about, the end result would be undesirable! This is also the case with depression - once someone understands what it is and what can be done to help, this will equip them with the information that is needed to get better and stay better.

Asking others' experiences....reading books and articles that may offer good information...checking out websites...asking the doctor for good books or references to follow up...listening to recommended audio tapes/CD's...checking out any local or national self-help organisations. All of these can provide useful information.

Get support -
USE your support

This is not an easy task, particularly to see through on one's own. Someone who has lost touch with people they once found good company or helpful could get back in touch and try to be as open with them as possible. It's amazing how people can rally round to help...but they may need asking...and one may need to be more open about what's been going on. Such support can be friends, acquaintances, family members. Don't forget, one's own doctor or practice nurse are also there to assist. People WANT to help.

Keeping an eye out for local or national support groups, if that's something that might be of interest, is worthwhile. Not everyone likes groups but some people find it very rewarding to talk and share experiences with others. There are also helplines and agencies (see back of this book).

Talk, express, share, DON'T BOTTLE!

...UNSAID THINGS....
..UNRESOLVED PAST..
..BOTTLED ANGER....
CHRONIC WORRY......
..IGNORED PROBLEMS..
..UNSPOKEN RAGE....

Depression fills the mind with all sorts of thoughts, feelings and emotions…bottling these up only adds to the problem and indeed may make the depression worse, or keep it going for a lot longer. It's not always easy for some to talk about what's going on inside, but it is an essential part of getting better. Whether it's to someone known personally or to a professional - finding someone to talk to, somewhere, is important. Sometimes a personal friend or relative is not enough, and it may be that a counsellor (via the GP), a psychologist or a psychiatrist may be the next step to dealing with some of the unpleasant or self-destructive thoughts. A doctor will be able to guide and advise on this. It is not a backward step - it's sometimes the start of regaining your life

BOTTLES GO 'POP' - TALKING RELIEVES TENSION!

The STOP technique

It is important to try and **STOP** the thoughts, feelings and behaviours that you indulge in that contribute to you feeling bad. Unless you catch yourself indulging in these self-defeating reactions it may be difficult, even impossible, to get yourself out of the gloom. Practise catching these self-destructive and self-induced habits.

You cannot catch them all, but you **CAN** catch many of them before they get a hold of you - once they get a hold, it's a downward spiral! Start talking to yourself; be firm, get in **EARLY** before the really bad thoughts, feelings and behaviours take you over.

Activity

Depression, and the chemical imbalances in the body, cause a person to slow down...stop doing things...avoid...reduce social contact. This in turn makes that person feel even worse. It is very important to re-start activity gradually. This <u>doesn't</u> mean start doing aerobics and 22 hours in the gym - it's about a **slow** and **gradual** increase in <u>pleasurable</u> activities.

Try doing one or more of the following, for just 5 or 10 minutes per day:

o   A gentle walk around the block
o   A short bicycle ride
o   Walk to the shops instead of driving
o   A brief swim or short gentle workout
o   Work in the garden
o   Start a new project..in the garden/in the house/with a friend
o   A short physical stretching/deep breathing routine

You have some responsibility to kick-start your body!

Rest and relaxation

<u>Depression is exhausting</u> - people who have not been through it sometimes don't really understand this. "But you don't **DO** anything - how can you be tired?". The chemical imbalances cause extreme tiredness on their own, but the emotional fatigue is also present thinking 'bad' thoughts and being upset or down is mentally taxing!

Someone who is depressed does not always seek 'permission' to stop and rest - they **<u>NEED</u>** to rest and relax, as this helps the body and mind recover it's strength, just as in any other physical illness! It is important however, to balance this with short bursts of activity, as detailed previously. Rest and relaxation on their own are not enough - this has to be complemented by activity and increased physical movement.

We all need a cave once in a while

Whether it is at work or at home, we all need somewhere to simply disappear into, to re-charge, to escape for a while, to be ourselves. Not having a cave can be extremely exhausting and frustrating. Many people invent caves just to have somewhere to go.

Even in the best relationships, in the best jobs, people need a **place of their own.** Have **YOU** got one? If not, can you create one without annoying everyone else. Good relationships allowS partners to have a little cave once in a while, as long as (a) it helps you (b) its therapeutic (energising), and (c) <u>you don't stay in there too long!</u>

"Time out!"

It's probably helpful to tell others around you that you are intending to have moments of "Time out"…pointing out that you are also going to try and balance this with the same amount of increased activity. Consider anything that helps you relax.

What about:

- o   Soak in a nice aromatherapy bath
- o   Put your feet up in front of a good film
- o   Get back into the habit of listening to music
- o   Start a new book…get some magazines
- o   Start writing some letters…start a diary
- o   Close your eyes and re-live a nice holiday
- o   Take a short break away
- o   Try out some aromatherapy, reflexology or massage
- o   Have a pamper evening or day
- o   Go shopping…just don't spend too much!

Express yourself

It's not always the right time to talk to someone, but there's still a need to get your thoughts out. There are many powerful ways of expressing your thoughts and feelings, so consider some of the following:

o Start a journal or diary…write it daily or as and when you want to.

o Write some letters…say what you WANT to say (just don't send them!). This is particularly good if you have a certain person in mind that has caused you a lot of grief!

o Keep a diary with columns of 'Thoughts', 'Feelings', and 'Behaviours'…start to understand the different components that make up your state of mind..these are things to try and change - one might be the cause of the other?

o Art or crafts…paint, draw, pottery, stitching, building something, poetry, write a book, start a family tree…..

The importance of
PLEASURE AND ACHIEVEMENT

These two things become less or absent when someone becomes depressed. Worst of all, people start to do things that actually make them unhappy (DISpleasure) and lower their sense of self esteem (UNDER-achievement). It is essential, therefore, to increase pleasure and achievement to counter the feelings of depression and lowered confidence.

THINGS THAT GIVE ME
PLEASURE

1) SOAK IN A BATH
2) A GENTLE MASSAGE
3) BEING TAKEN OUT
4) MEETING WITH DAD

THINGS THAT GIVE ME
A SENSE OF ACHIEVEMENT

1) DOING SOME HOME COOKING
2) SORTING THE SHED OUT
3) WRITING SOME LETTERS
4) CATCHING UP WITH STUDY

Consider: what activities did you once do, that you've now stopped doing, that **DID** give you a sense of pleasure and a feeling of achievement? What have you **STOPPED DOING?** Plan, and start to build into the day, activities that are pleasurable, that make you feel better, that relax you, that make you smile, that improve your mood, even if it only lasts for a few moments. **DO IT MORE!** What things make you feel as if you have done something worthwhile? An activity that gives you a sense of **VALUE** even if it doesn't give you much pleasure? **DO IT MORE!**

Maybe even make a couple of **lists** over the next few days or weeks:

Things that give me pleasure: _____ ?
Things that give me a sense of achievement: _____ ?

Problem solving

It is all too easy to lump all problems together - and see it all as one big impossible problem. For instance:

"My whole life is awful!"
"Everything at work is terrible!"
"My relationship is ALL crap!"
"The whole house needs a bulldozer!"

When **ALL** problems are lumped together, it can seem like an **ELEPHANT** of a problem...HUGE, INSURMOUNTABLE, IMPOSSIBLE! It's important to **a)** Regain a perspective, **b)** Break it all down into manageable chunks, and **c)** Work through it methodically.

Some problems are indeed difficult, but many are not - if dealt with individually and separately. Do the next part over the next few days or weeks...take your time, don't rush it. Even better, **write it all down.**

Start working through the following steps, slowly and with thought:

1. List **ALL** the problems.

2. Now re-write these same problems, but put them into a list of what's the BIGGEST and what's the SMALLEST. This is called a **Priority List**....a **grading** of all the problems.

3. Now **choose a problem to work on** - best to start with the <u>SMALLEST or EASIEST problem first.</u> Don't start with the biggest/hardest!

4. Now list **ALL THE POSSIBLE OPTIONS** that there are for this problem - don't hold back, list <u>EVERYTHING</u> from the silliest to the most realistic.

5. Now, going through this whole list of options, write down ALL the **ADVANTAGES** and **DISADVANTAGES** of each option.

6. Having now looked at all the options and seen the advantages and disadvantages of each - **CHOOSE WHICH OPTION** you are going to try. Do NOT choose an option that you KNOW is something you cannot deal with...be realistic and practical.

7. Now, with this option in mind, make a detailed **PLAN** of **HOW YOU ARE GOING TO CARRY THIS OUT**. Take your time with this step - don't miss any detail out that might help you achieve this plan of action...
consider: how / when / who's involved / practical details.

8. Now **CARRY OUT THE PLAN.**

9. Once done, how did it go?

If it goes 'pear-shaped' where did it all go wrong? Did you miss a detail? Trace back to where it started to go wrong and re-do it from that step, try again. If it went well, move onto the next problem and go through the same steps. Sometimes working this through with a friend can be helpful - but you must only do want YOU feel you can do…don't be bullied into anything!

The importance of diet and fluids

Depression involves chemical changes in the body - these chemicals are also affected by what one eats and drinks. All too often people get into the habit of digesting things that actually make mood drop and anxiety feelings increase badly affecting their ability to cope.

Try to increase:

o   Water intake - dehydration is remarkably common, makes one feel tired and can be the main cause of headaches.

o   Fresh food, especially fruit. Fibre foods and high vitamin foods.

o   High protein foods to improve energy.

Try to reduce:

o   Alcohol and 'recreational' drugs - these lower mood/energy.

o   Tea and coffee - these cause anxiety symptoms, irritability, poor concentration and sleeplessness.

o   High sugar, fatty and salty foods. Reduce convenience foods.

Some people eat less when they become depressed (weight can be lost), but some 'comfort' eat (weight gain). Watch what you consume!

Sleep

Depression is a different experience for everyone...some people sleep all the time (hypersomnia) and others hardly get a good sleep most nights (insomnia). It's not the amount of sleep one gets, it's the **quality** of the sleep that matters most. Most people who become depressed have RUMINATIONS - theses are thoughts, usually not very good ones, that just won't go away; they go round and round in the mind. Such thoughts can do several things:

1) Cause you to stay awake, despite being tired the worrying thoughts stop you getting off to sleep.
2) Waken you up from sleep (often at early hours of the morning).

Ruminatory thinking stops DEEP SLEEP from occurring and it causes shallow sleep. So even if someone DOES sleep for 10 hours, they awaken in a very tired state. If these thoughts stop you getting to sleep, but eventually you drift off...the quality of sleep is still poor.

This is why, whether you sleep a lot or don't get much sleep…you constantly feel tired. Other things can also cause poor sleep, such as:

o   Drinking too much tea/coffee.
o   Eating too late at night.
o   Taking antidepressants at the wrong time of the day.
o   Certain medications for other conditions (see your doctor).
o   Not being physically tired enough (too little physical activity).

TRY:
- Write things down on a regular basis (to get rid of the thoughts).
- Talk things through with someone regularly (empty your head!).
- Have a good diet - reduce things that are unhelpful for sleep.
- Develop a good pattern for the evening, that will HELP sleep

PAMPER, PAMPER, PAMPER!

Children need to either wait until their parents reward them, or they have to seek permission for 'treats'.....adults are not children any more, and can and SHOULD treat themselves more! Show yourself more respect by being nicer to yourself. It's always nice being treated by others...but don't wait for it - do it as much as you can....

Don't wait for a reason to treat yourself..you ARE the reason!
Are there things you USED to do that you've stopped doing?
Are there NEW things you'd like to try?
Plan these things into the day, into the week.
You OWE it to yourself, don't feel guilty about it!

Surely it's about
POSITIVE THINKING?

There has been a lot written about "Positive Thinking", but so-called positive thinking is what children do ..they are living in an unrealistic world that has a cheery gloss on everything! What is more helpful is REALISTIC THINKING.

Realistic thinking provides us with less chance of failure and disappointment - positive thinking is simply too high a standard to achieve! - so do not be tempted to feed depressed people with a shiny happy view of things as it will only come over as trite and nauseous! Keep things in the REAL world.

Are there ALTERNATIVES?
YES!

Conventional (western) medicine is a relatively new invention. For thousands of years there have been many other therapies practised by the ancients, therapies that we now call Alternative Therapies. Although the evidence varies and is sometimes absent, there can be no doubt that many people benefit greatly from the range of therapies that are around today. Consider trying these out and, even better, build them into your daily life.

Why not try:

o   Aromatherapy (Burning oils/incense, bath oils, massage).
o   Reflexology (Foot massage).
o   Indian Head Massage (Head massage with oils).
o   Remedial massage / deep muscle massage.
o   Self-hypnosis / visualisation techniques.

Your doctor or nurse might be able to provide you with information about where to obtain these treatments. Also look in your local paper or on the internet, but try to use people who have either been recommended or are well-known as good therapists.

Summary of (self-help) approaches for MILD Depression

o   Always acknowledge how you feel…to yourself and to others.

o   Monitor yourself over time…don't fall into previous 'bad habits'.

o   Understand what is going on - get information/ask questions.

o   Get some good sources of information…books/tapes/CD's/ World Wide Web.

o   Create more support for yourself…and use it!

o   Avoid isolating yourself…don't have too much time by yourself.

o   Gently increase activities you enjoy.

o   Are there things you've stopped doing? If so - restart them

o   Relax more - have stops and breaks in the day.

o   Get those thoughts and feelings OUT. Don't BOTTLE UP!

o   Try and find someone you can be open and honest with.

o   Try writing things down…a journal or a diary.

o   Try being creative…poetry / art?

o   Increase the pleasure activities in the day.

o   Increase activities that give a sense of achievement.

o   Try using a 'Problem Solving' approach for some problems (See Appendix)

o   Look at your diet and fluid intake…does it need changing?

o   Have adequate sleep and rest. Avoid stimulants and excessive alcohol etc.

o   Pamper yourself regularly - don't wait for it to come to you!

o   Look into alternative therapies…try them out.

Antidepressants may be needed, but they are not the whole answer. There are things we need to do for ourselves if we are to get better…and STAY better. It's about building into your every day life techniques and approaches that have either been lost, or have simply been stopped. It's also a time to consider new things to try. You may need to take stock of how you run your life.

Always be guided by your doctor or nurse. There are **always** people around to help, use them. One day **YOU** might be able to offer help.

The Magic Tablets!

In this 'quick-fix' society that we live in, it seems that the easiest option is always the favourite choice for many people whether it's a cold, backache, flu or depression: **"Take a tablet!"**

What would we do without the **pills** that are provided for us in pharmacies, health food shops, supermarkets and at the doctor's? This is not to say that all tablets and medications are not helpful - but we are increasingly becoming demanding of medication prescribed or otherwise as the solution for everything. It isn't. Tablets and medication do have their place <u>but they don't solve problems!</u>

From the doctor's point of view

Often due to time restrictions, and simply not knowing what else to do, the prescription pad is the first port of call.

The prescription can also be what the patient expects, in fact many people are disappointed when they DON'T get a prescription! Doctors are finding that their patients can get quite difficult if they are not given a prescription, it's what they've come for! This can also be the problem with other health related problems such as infections…people EXPECT to get antibiotics - many people do not fully understand that antibiotics are NOT the answer for all infections!

Antidepressants are NOT the answer to all forms of depression

Pills are for symptoms....
talking is for problems!

Antidepressants will only ease the symptoms of moderate to severe depression - they should NOT be prescribed for MILD depression. Because of this, it can be all too easy to just hand out a pill as an apparent 'cure', when it isn't.

Mild to moderate depression still needs help, but NOT medication. Mild to moderate depression is a <u>normal response</u> to problems - all humans experience this from time to time - it should NOT be a reason to give prescribed medication. However, consultation time is limited for a busy GP (many GP's see themselves as pill dispensers!), and to give a pill can save time but it doesn't: badly treated depression only makes the illness carry on for longer, and causes more longer-term problems - <u>it's a false economy to just give a pill!</u>

Antidepressants

We already know that in depression there is an imbalance of chemicals - antidepressants simply correct that imbalance but they don't work straight away, and pills on their own are not always the answer.

Just as insulin is needed by some diabetics to correct their insulin imbalance - diet has also got to be part of their treatment. Insulin alone is not the answer <u>diabetics need to make other changes in their diet and lifestyle in order to stay well.</u> This is the same with depression - pills are only part of the answer: other changes need to be made, including diet, lifestyle and addressing the causes.

There are still many myths about antidepressants

All of the above are **WRONG!** Always ask for good advice from your doctor , don't just believe what you read or what you are told by others!

Antidepressants are completely different from tranquillisers - tranquillisers are addictive, antidepressants are not although one or two can cause some problems coming off them, but by far most of them are not problematic.

Some facts about antidepressants

○ All antidepressants take a few weeks to start working & improving mood - but side effects will start straight away, so you might feel a little worse before you feel better. This is normal and to be expected.

○ All medications have side effects - antidepressants are no exception. Some side effects are helpful, some are not. They will ease(don't be put off by what's written in the pack!).

○ Antidepressants need to be taken at the FULL dose, for at least 8 to 12 months…AFTER you start to feel better. Don't stop them! If you've had many episodes, you may need to take them for longer periods or indefinitely - check with your doctor.

○ Don't stop them because you don't feel better immediately / you feel a little worse at first / or because you feel fine…see the treatment through! Always be guided by your doctor.

○ Reduce alcohol when taking this medication. Alcohol is itself a depressant, so only take a drink occasionally.

○ Stop using all 'recreational' drugs (e.g. cannabis) when on antidepressants, but don't stop other prescribed medication without speaking to your doctor first.

○ To help with side effects (e.g. dry mouth / constipation) - increase water/fluids (not alcohol!) and eat plenty fibre. Ask for advice.

○ Do not take antidepressants with other 'health foods', vitamins/supplements or natural alternatives without seeking advice first.

○ **REMEMBER:** Pills are only PART of the answer - to get better quicker (and STAY better), you also need to look at your lifestyle, diet and activities, as well as addressing any problems that may have caused your depression. Don't just rely on the medication to sort everything, it won't!

Natural antidepressants?

Health food shops and the internet are full of possible remedies for depression including dietary supplements, vitamins and herbal substances. Some can be helpful, some are not.....

There is some evidence that HYPERICUM (St. John's Wort) and 5HTP are helpful for MILD to MODERATE depression. Do NOT take these alongside prescribed medications. These too have some minor side effects and reasons why some shouldn't take them, please seek advice. Don't overdo it with vitamin and 'healthy' supplements - these can also be harmful if taken inappropriately. Like antidepressants, Hypericum and 5HTP need to be taken at the correct dose, and for the same length of time.

Preventing a relapse or sliding back, or getting re-infected by the depression virus!

Don't get complacent! The virus may look for the same route back - has the original cause been sorted? Are you safe from re-infection?

Some TIPS:

o   Be aware of any warning signs early!

o   Watch for any tell tale signs of sliding back.

o   Try not to repeat old mistakes..don't go down the previous path that led you to your depression.

o   Learn to say "STOP!"…draw a line earlier!

o   Make sure you have a good support ready to hand.

o   Take stock…what needs to change? Are you changing it?

o   Try to get more of a balance…work/play/pleasure/rest/etc.

Lessons to be learned

Suffering from depression is not all bad - it is at the time, but most people come out the other end **wiser** and **more knowledgeable** about themselves. Strength is gained - inner strength, insight and an increased ability to cope. People who have not gone through such experiences do not know their limitations, have no idea of how far they can be pushed, and do not know their own warning signs that something's wrong, people who have gone through depression and anxiety DO know these things.

So, although the experience of depression is painful, it is a wiser person that emerges from the blackness. Remember too that if the virus is detected, and caught early - it will be prevented from demolishing the internal immune system. If contained, it will also not infect anyone else! If nothing is learned…it will re-infect!

Comfort Zone

Is it time to step out of the Comfort Zone?

Have you got the support and energy to do this?

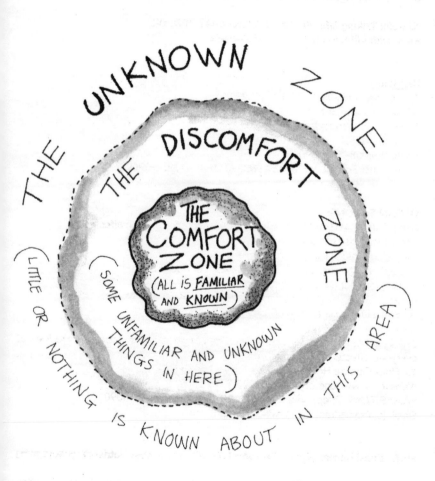

THE UNKNOWN ZONE

THE DISCOMFORT ZONE

THE COMFORT ZONE (ALL IS *FAMILIAR* AND **KNOWN**)

(SOME UNFAMILIAR AND UNKNOWN THINGS IN HERE)

(LITTLE OR NOTHING IS KNOWN ABOUT IN THIS AREA)

RESOURCES

CDs and Tapes:

o   Coping with Depression (CD or Audio Cassettes)

o   Coping with Anxiety (CD or Audio Cassette)

o   Feeling Good (Self Esteem & Assertiveness Skills) (CD or Audio Cassettes)

o   The Relaxation Kit (Cd or Audio Cassettes)

All from: **Talking Life, PO Box 1, Wirral CH47 7DD, UK.**
www.talkinglife.co.uk Tel: 0151-632-0662

Helplines:
Depression Alliance 0845 123 23 20
MIND: MindinfoLine
Open Monday to Friday 9.15am to 5.15pm
0845 766 0163
SANE LINE 0845 767 8000
Samaritans: Telephone: 08457 909090 Text: 07725 909090

ORGANISATIONS:
DEPRESSION ALLIANCE is the leading UK charity for people affected by
depression. 0845 123 23 20
www.depressionalliance.org
212 Spitfire Studios, 63 - 71 Collier Street, London N1 9BE
Email: information@depressionalliance.org
MIND is the leading mental health charity in England and Wales.
PO Box 277, Manchester, M60 3XN info@mind.org.uk
www.mind.org.uk
SANE is one of the UK's leading charities concerned with improving the lives of
everyone affected by mental illness
1st Floor Cityside House, 40 Adler Street, London, E1 1EE
Website: www.sane.org.uk Tel: 020 7375 1002
SAMARITANS: Telephone: 08457 909090 Text: 07725 909090
Email: jo@samaritans.org www.samaritans.org

Professional bodies (Counsellors/Mental health teams/Psychiatrists/Psychologists)

Yourself: You are your OWN resource, never forget what is already inside waiting
to be accessed and used!

Other useful reading

Sod It All!	Martin Davies
Manage your Mind	Gillian Butler & Tony Hope
Who Moved My Cheese?	Dr Spencer Johnson
Toxic Parents	Dr Susan Forward
Down with Gloom	Professor Brice Pitt
Living with a Stranger	Valerie Stillwell
Counselling for Toads	Robert de Board
The New Mood Therapy	Dr David Burns
What Stress in the Workplace	Ruth Chambers & Martin Davies
So Young, so Sad, so Listen	Philip Graham & Carol Hughes

For Health Professionals (GPs, Nurses and Therapists)

The WHO guide to Mental Health in Primary Care Health in Primary Care (ICD-10 Guides) Published by: Royal Society of Medicine

SOD IT ALL! *How to Deal with the Stress 'Virus' in your Life*
by
Martin Davies

There are many books on stress - but none quite like this! Written by Martin Davies, author of 'Sod It! The Depression 'Virus' and how to Deal with It'. Easy to read and digest, informative and practical, whenever and wherever you have stress in your life, you need this book.

If all else fails, practise the ancient art of:

Sometimes there is simply nothing you can do to sort something out. Sometimes you <u>ARE</u> powerless. Some things may not be very fair or pleasant, but in the end we either moan about it pulling us down even further, or hit out at it and we lose our dignity and the respect of others, or we have to accept it.

Practise saying '**SOD IT!**'

APPENDIX
The 10 Diary Templates that can help!

As discussed in the previous chapters, writing your thoughts, feelings and experiences down can be very helpful. Doing this can:

o   Help to <u>empty your head </u>of difficult/confusing/upsetting things.
o   Provide <u>vital information</u> about yourself - **for** yourself.
o   Help you to <u>monitor</u> progress, setbacks and learning.
o   <u>Improve insight</u> and personal awareness.
o   Be a <u>relief!</u> (It saves building it all up inside)
o   Be helpful to others you care to share it with.

You might wish to make up your own way of writing things down. Play around with different ways of emptying your thoughts, feelings, reactions and personal observations. You have information inside of yourself, what a waste to let it remain in a place that does you no good. **YOU** are a **RESOURCE** for **YOURSELF**.
The clues are inside!

Diary template 1.
The MOOD Diary

Just take a note of how your mood is (on a scale of zero to ten - where 0 = very low and 10 = very good). You can do this at the start and end of each day, or periodically throughout the day, look to see how your mood changes. Try and see ifthere are any triggers that lower/improve your mood.

Diary template 2.
The THOUGHTS Diary

Simply try and get into the habit of identifying 'troublesome' thoughts - and note them down. Unless you are aware of these thoughts, they will infect the rest of your thinking!

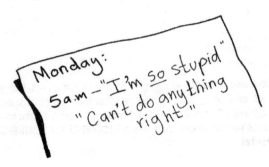

Diary template 3.
The FEELINGS Diary

Whenever you get a **strong** feeling (say over 5 on a zero to ten scale) - write about it, what exact feeling is it, what happened, how long did it last? Try and influence your own mood by altering your thoughts or actions.

Monday: 10.30 —
"ANGER" — Mum came
(8/10)   round and said
          the house was
                filthy!!

Diary template 4.
The BEHAVIOUR Diary

Try and identify behaviours (actions/activities) that either make you feel worse, and **B)** that make you feel better. Try to do MORE of **B** and LESS of **A**

MONDAY:
3pm — Had a soak in bath
      before kids came home.
      (FELT RELAXED)
4.30pm — Rushed to shops
        (FELT STRESSED / ANGRY)

Diary template 5.
The LINKING Diary

This is combining diaries **1, 2, 3,** and **4.** Make columns and See if you can see any **links** or patterns between each of your thoughts, feelings, behaviours and the effects on your mood. Can you try to influence/change these?

MONDAY: Thought	Feeling	Behaviour	MOOD:
"I really messed that all up"	stupid inadequate	Wept— then hid away	2/10

Diary template 6.
The EMPTY-MY-HEAD Diary

Just get ANY thoughts out of your head...in any order, it doesn't matter. You might find all the negative pours out first - try and move towards including positive stuff too.

MONDAY: When I went into work everyone was so down. No matter who I spoke to they were all so miserable. I ended up hiding away and then when David....

Diary template 7.
The LETTER Diary

If you have a conflict or unresolved issue with a person, then write an **honest, open** and **frank** letter to this person. <u>Hold nothing back</u> - **SAY** what you **WANT** to really say **just don't send it!** At least, not immediately. Get your honest sentiments out then put it aside for a while, then decide what to do with it (re-write it/expand on it/tear it up/send it?).

> Dear Dad,
> When I came over last week you snapped at me! How <u>dare</u> you talk to me like that! I'd like to......

Diary template 8.
The POETRY Diary

This is a variation of Letter Writing - it is just more creative and suits some. Having to **create** poetry requires a good deal of concentration...this can assist with getting rid of unpleasant feelings and thoughts. Always date and time each poem and try to keep them. Look back and reflect on these later.

> 10/6/06 (10.30pm)
> Why are you such a bore....
> Living with you –
> Is <u>such</u> a chore!

Diary template 9.
The PLEASURE/VALUE Diary

For a day or so (a week if you can), note down in 2 columns the activities you do, noting down the LEVEL (0 to 10 scale) of **A)** PLEASURE and **B)** VALUE (achievement) you feel. Look back and try and increase the activities that gave you **more** pleasure/feeling of satisfaction. Remember, that some activities will give you pleasure but no sense of value - that's OK. Some activities will give you a sense of achievement but little or no pleasure - that's OK too.

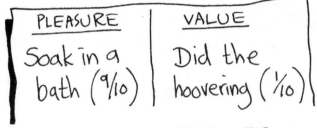

PLEASURE	VALUE
Soak in a bath (9/10)	Did the hoovering (1/10)

Diary template 10.
The LIFE EVENTS Diary

Over a period of days or weeks, list down, starting with as far back as you can remember, any events that have taken place in your life that were **significant** to you (good or bad)...events/changes/memories etc. Try and put them in order of when they occurred (earliest.........most recent). Are there any repeating themes (e.g. loss/change), or can you see from your list **WHY** you feel the way you do - there are REASONS! Try it out.

1980 – Got divorced
1982 – Moved house
1987 – Lost job
1992 – Diagnosed with diabetes

Activity diary

For 1 week record your daily activities

Try and rate how you enjoyed doing these things on a scale of 1-10
(1=not very much; 10=really enjoyed this activity)

	Sunday	Monday	Tuesday	Wednesday	Thursday	Friday	Saturday
9-10 a.m.							
10-11							
11-12							
12-1							
1-2							
2-3							
3-4							
4-5							
5-6							
6-7							
7-8							
8-12							

What activity helped in the past?
What activity helps now?
What activity does not help?
Plan in more activities in your week that make you feel better.

A brief guide to essential oils

PROPERTIES:	ESSENTIAL OIL:	CONDITION RELIEVED:
SEDATIVE:	Lavender Chamomile Marjoram	Stress/anxiety/ irritability/anger/ insomnia
UPLIFTING:	Jasmine Clary sage Grapefruit	Moodiness/ depression/lack confidence
INVIGORATING:	Juniper Rosemary Cardamom	Lethargy/boredom/ immune deficiency
APHRODISIAC:	Ylang Ylang Patchouli Jasmine	Shyness/frigidity/ emotional coldness/ impotence
REGULATING: **(mood)**	Bergamot Geranium Frankincense	Mood swings/anxiety with depression/ menstrual imbalance
MENTAL STIMULATION:	Lemon Peppermint Black pepper	Poor concentration/ mental fatigue/ poor memory

(Courtesy of Chris Knecht, Alternative Therapist)

What readers have said about this book

"A comprehensive resource for people who are affected by depression"
(Practice Nursing magazine)

"Having worked with depression in primary care for over 10 years, it has been a constant frustration to me that no-one has combined the wisdom of the experience of depression with the humour and self-deprecation needed for recovery. This skinny little tome changes all that. Humour is anti-viral... buy this book for sustained immunity!!"

"This is really helpful for anyone who suffers from depression themselves, or has family members, friends or colleagues who suffer. It is easy to read and 'dip into' (really important as the ability to concentrate tends to go while depressed) while being very informative and based on research. The diary templates are really helpful, especially 7. The cartoons are really fabulous and convey so much information so simply"

"If this book had been around during my years of coping with depression I would have been able to explain to the people nearest to me exactly what I was going through and not felt that I was some kind of freak, drop out, a changed person. I am convinced that the illustrations would have brought a smile to my face and the whole world (well, my world) wouldn't have been so bad"

"This is a very accessible read that is brought to life by the perceptive and humourous cartoons. Conceptualising depression as a "virus" is an interesting and visual way to convey the debilitating experience. It clarifies fact from fiction and lets you dip into features that may be pertinent to you in surviving depression"

Also in the "SOD IT" Series

SOD IT ALL!

How to Deal with the Stress 'Virus' in your Life

WHY GET THIS BOOK?

There are many books on stress - but none quite like this!
IT IS: easy to read and digest, whilst being informative and practical.
IT IS NOT: full of academic jargon and confusing 'psycho-babble'! Most books on stress are repetitive, predictable or highly personalised; this one is filled with cartoons and as little text as possible. The cartoons, however, do not trivialise, they enhance the reader's understanding of the facts as well as raise a smile, particularly when they remind you of someone – or yourself!

WHO IS IT FOR?

YOU – if you simply want to know more, to understand stress, or if you have suffered (or are suffering from) stress-related difficulties; to help you understand or cope with a friend or family member, or a colleague at work. This is for you.
THEM – for a family member or friend; if you are a professional or counsellor wishing to provide your patient/client with easy and engaging information; to help someone acknowledge stress and to move forward to help them. This is for them.

FACT OR FICTION?

This book is based on research evidence and personal accounts and experiences. The author, Martin Davies, has both training and experience of treating people with stress-related problems, as well as many years training professionals in the field. Martin would agree that he is not, himself, the most relaxed of persons; he has to work hard to manage his stress. There is nothing in this book that he does not practise himself. His illustrations are, in themselves, a form of self-therapy!

This easy-to-read book will show you how to:

- **Recognise and understand the stress 'viruses'**
- **Deal with stress more effectively**
- **Keep your mind healthier and keep further 'infection' away**
- **Be ready to deal with stress and pressure in the future**

Discover today how to beat the Stress 'Virus' and keep your mind healthy and happy.

SOD IT! BOOKS

Is the book imprint of Talking Life, specialists in Health Information CDs and audio cassettes and designers of training for healthcare and other public sector staff. Self-help titles include Depression, Anxiety, Pain Management, Sleep Problems, Bereavement, Stress, Headaches & Migraine, Tranquilliser Addiction, Self Esteem and Assertiveness Skills. There is also a popular range of Relaxation programmes. For latest information about the **sod-it.co.uk** range of books, contact us on 0151-632-0662, write to us at PO Box 1, Wirral, CH47 7DD or visit our website:

www.sod-itbooks.co.uk

Find out about our range of CDs, tapes and seminars at:

www.talkinglife.co.uk